Yin Yang Primer

A Guide to the Unifying Principle of Macrobiotics

Edward Esko

Foreword by Alex Jack

One Peaceful World Press
Becket, Massachusetts

Dedication
For Daniel and his siblings, friends, and members
of his generation. May they change the world
to one of health and peace.

Yin Yang Primer
A Guide to the Unifying Principle of Macrobiotics
© 2000 by Edward Esko

One Peaceful World Press
P.O. Box 10
Leland Road
Becket, MA 01223
U.S.A.

Toll-Free in the U.S. 1-888-322-4095
Telephone (413) 623-2322
Fax (413) 623-6042

First Edition: February 2000

10 9 8 7 6 5 4 3 2 1

ISBN 1–882984–38–2
Printed in U.S.A.

Contents

Yin Areba Yang

Yin areba yang
Yang areba yin
Yama taka kereba
Tanifukashi

Yin o tenjite yang
Yang o tenjite yin
Nan ari sunawachi
Arigatashi

Wherever there is yin there is yang.
Wherever there is yang there is yin
The higher the mountain
The deeper the valley

Let us change yin into yang
Let us change yang into yin
For any difficulties
We are always grateful.

—George Ohsawa

1
Foreword

Modern society has developed incredible technologies that can reach into deepest space and penetrate the DNA of cells. The Internet allows us to communicate with people instantaneously around the world, and jet planes enable us to enjoy breakfast in London, lunch in New York, and dinner in Tokyo. Despite these impressive advances, we lack a unifying principle to maintain our daily health and happiness and understand the world in comprehensive, dynamic terms.

In the ancient world, the complementary opposite energies of the cosmos were traditionally known as heaven's and earth's forces. Different cultures and civilizations knew these polarities under various names. In the Far East, they were called *yin* and *yang*. The Greeks referred to them as *love* and *strife*. In the Gospel of Thomas, Jesus referred to them as *activity* and *rest*. Today, we find yin/yang tendencies referred to in literature as *Apollonian* and *Dionysian*, in science as *cathode* and *anode*, *electron* and *proton*, *infrared* and *ultraviolet*, in economics as *bear market* and *bull market*, and in contemporary social parlance as *Type A* and *Type B personalities*, *hawks* and *doves*, and *macho* and *fem*.

By whatever name, these energies form the canvass on which our whole life is lived. Light and dark, hot and cold, man and woman, fire and water, and other fundamental polarities are all basic manifestations of yin and yang. These energies are not mystical forces, hidden away, accessible only after years of seeking enlightenment and chewing each mouthful of food 300 times. These are the ever present energies of daily life, intuitively understood by children as well as grandparents, the birthright of us all.

Over the last generation, modern macrobiotics has reintroduced yin and yang as a dynamic, practical tool of understanding, classification, and analysis. Hotels, schools, hospitals, nursing homes, and prisons are now actively serving macrobiotic products to their staffs, clientele, and the general public. In Washington, D.C., the Smithsonian Institution opened a permanent collection at the National Museum of American History recognizing macrobiotics as the catalyst and spearhead for the natural, organic foods movement and alternative and complementary medicine in the United States. From Boston to Sydney, from San Francisco to Beijing, from Denver to New Delhi, macrobiotic principles are guiding society toward a healthier, more peaceful way of life as the new century begins. Yin and yang is the native language of atoms, cells, tissues, organs, individual species, ecosystems, stars, constellations, galaxies—life itself. It is the Esperanto of macrobiotics and the international holistic community.

Edward Esko, the author of this book, has been one of the most active contemporary macrobiotic teachers over the last twenty-five years, lecturing and counseling in Europe, Asia, Latin America, and throughout North America and prolifically writing and editing books and articles. Building on the teachings of George Ohsawa, Michio Kushi, Herman Aihara, and other pioneers, he has applied yin and yang—the universal principles of spirallic change and harmony—to helping individuals and families address personal health concerns, as well as helping society resolve problems related to crime and violence, the environmental crisis, and war and peace. In these pages, he introduces concepts of *spiralgenesis* and *spiralconsciousness* that take yin and yang to new levels.

Yin Yang Primer will introduce you to the principles of universal complementarity, show how to classify all phenomena, and enable you to begin to look at life in terms of dynamic, flowing energy and vibration, rather than fixed, material objects. A variety of charts listing scores of examples is included for deeper study and reflection. *Yin Yang Primer* is your passport to a long, healthy life. Coming into possession of this little book is better than winning the world's biggest lottery. In your hands lie the key to health and happiness, the compass to peace and joy. With the unifying principle of yin and yang, you can overcome all difficulties, harmonize all relationships, and realize your biggest dreams. I hope you will apply it wisely to begin a new spiral in your life, a spiral of balance and harmony that contributes to transforming the planet as a whole.

Alex Jack
Becket, Massachusetts
September 17, 1999

Chapter One
Commonness and Difference

One truth, many appearances.
—Becket, Massachusetts, April, 1999

All things have the same fundamental nature. Let us take as examples a pencil, desk, book, and plant. Each exists within time and space; they have this in common. Since they exist here and now, on earth at the present time, they share a tiny segment of the infinity of time and space. They have a form, and that form is defined by shape, size, color, weight, density, and other characteristics.

These objects are composed of elements. Elements are formed by the union of electrons, protons, and other preatomic particles. Preatomic particles are made up of energy. They are not solid. As an old Buddhist sutra states, "form is emptiness, and emptiness form."

Everything is ultimately energy. The atoms that make up each object are in a constant state of motion. Each object ultimately changes. All things are ephemeral, existing for a brief moment within the endless ocean of time.

Attributes such as these are common to all things, from galaxies to atoms, stars to cells, mist to ice crystals, and elephants to bacteria. All things share a common origin—the universe—and pass through a life cycle defined by a beginning, middle, and end, followed by a new beginning in a different form. Everything is constantly changing.

At the same time, no two things are identical. Each thing or being is a unique manifestation of the universe. Perfect "sameness" does not exist, nor does perfect symmetry. To prove this to yourself, stand in front of a mirror with a blank piece of paper. Cover the right half of your face and look closely at the left. Then cover the left and observe the right. You may be shocked to see how different each side of your face is.

Things exist within time and space, yet no two things occupy the same position in time and space. While all physical objects are made of atoms and molecules, the number and combination of atoms and molecules in each is unique.

Let us return to the pencil, desk, book, and plant. We see that although they have color, texture, shape, density, and weight, these attributes are different in each. Although they are produced by elements found on earth, the elements that comprise each are different. The process in which each came into being is also unique. The pencil, table, and book are man-made, while the plant is created by nature. Each man-made object is made of wood, yet each is made of wood from a different tree. Each object has a use, yet each is used differently. Each has value, the value of each is different.

Human beings are perfect examples of the principle of commonness and difference. If we compare two people, we see they look alike and move in a similar way. People share functions such as breathing, eating, discharging waste, sleeping, and reproduction. They have a similar life cycle, beginning with birth, proceeding through growth, maturity, old age, and ending at death. They have a mother, father, and ancestors stretching back through time. Moreover, they share a common environment within a common time period. They have been exposed to the values, concepts, and lifestyles that characterize civilization. They have read many of the same books, seen the same movies, watched the same television programs, and eaten the same foods.

All people have physical needs for food, clothing, shelter, activity, and rest, and emotional needs for love, acceptance, and friendship. Everyone has a physical and spiritual nature. We all seek happiness and fulfillment.

At the same time, each person is unique. Each is born at a different time and in a different place, and each has a different size, weight, body build, hair color, and genetic makeup. Everyone's face is unique to him or her, as are facial expressions and mannerisms. Although we share basic functions, each of us has individual appetites and preferences. Each person breathes in a different way, pursues a different type of activity, and needs a specific amount of rest. Although the pattern of life is potentially the same for everyone, the way this pattern plays out differs from person to person.

We share a common environment, yet each of us occupies a different part of that environment. Time and space are unique to each individual. Although we have the same sense organs, each of us perceives the environment from our own individual perspective. Everyone has a life dream, but that dream is highly individual. Our dream is the result of the influence that each of us receives from our individual family background and environment. And although the pursuit of happiness is common to everyone, we all have our own individual definition of happiness. We can sum up by saying, "although we are all in the same boat, each passenger in the boat is different."

Our discussion now brings us to principles which express the truth of commonness and difference:

Commonness
1. Everything is a manifestation of one infinite universe.
(All beings and things share a common origin, the universe itself.)
2. Everything changes.
(Nothing is static. The universe is infinitely dynamic. All beings and things are constantly changing, they go through a process of creation, existence, and dissolution. Change is the only constant.)
3. What has a beginning has an end.
(Nothing is permanent; all beings and things eventually change form and emerge as something new. This process is without beginning or end.)

Difference
4. There is nothing identical.
(Even though all beings and things share a common origin and process of change, everything continually appears, changes form, and reappears in a way that is totally unique.)

Macrobiotic teachings derive from these universal principles. Macrobiotic dietary guidelines recognize the factors that are common to all, as well as the uniqueness of every individual. We live on planet earth, and must adapt our diet and lifestyle to our environment. We share a common evolutionary background, and as a result have the same body structure. We all share a common dietary heritage based on the intake of whole grains and vegetables as primary foods.

These factors are common to everyone. Macrobiotic dietary guidelines are based on these universal, common factors. Yet, while acknowledging the universal, macrobiotics respects the individual. The application of these principles is always individual and specific. When applying macrobiotic guidelines, we take into account individual differences based on as age, sex, activity, constitution, and condition. We also adapt these guidelines to endlessly varied climatic conditions and continual seasonal change.

An understanding of commonness and difference is essential not only in creating personal health, but in creating world health and world peace. In order to realize the dream of world peace, we must unite behind the common factors all human beings share, while respecting the endless diversity of human experience.

Chapter Two
Complementary Opposites

Difficult and easy complement each other.
Long and short exhibit each other.
High and low set measure to each other.
Voice and sound harmonize each other.
 —Lao Tsu

Everything exists because of complementary opposites. A chair, for example, is made of legs that project downward and a seat that faces upward. Each section of the chair—and the chair as a whole—contains an upper and lower part, a left and right side, a top and bottom, and an inside and outside. The opposites, or polarities, in each pair complement one another. Each pair of opposites is complementary to the others. Together they form the unity that makes up the chair.

Consider the polarities in a book. Books are composed of an outside and inside, a cover and contents. The front and back covers complement one another: the front is usually bold and direct, while the back is understated and detailed. When we open the book, it divides into left and right-hand pages, and each page has a front and a back side. The book is itself defined by the polarity between its left and right and upper and lower borders, its first and last pages, its beginning and end. Each page contains numerous complementary opposites. The pages contain text and illustrations, printed type and blank space, headings and text, words and punctuation, letters and numbers, vowels and consonants, nouns and verbs, and subjects and objects.

The law of economics, which governs the production and distribution of books, is driven by polarities. Economic activity is driven by the interplay between supply and demand, income and expense, and producer and consumer. In order to compete successfully, producers must keep their costs as low as possible, while charging the highest price for their products. Consumers are the polar opposite of producers. They would like to see producers spend as much as possible producing high-quality goods while paying as little as possible for them. The relationship between producer and consumer is good example of the complementarity existing between opposites. Both have the opposite orientation, yet both need each other.

Books, like everything else, do not exist in isolation. They exist in relation to other things and to the environment in general. These relationships are defined by complementary opposites. If we compare books, we see that some are thick, others thin, some are colorful, others plain, some are large, others small, some are interesting, others dull, some are read by many people, others by few. Complementary opposites also distinguish books from other objects, and make books and other things distinct from the environment as a whole.

The biological world exists because of polarity. Complementary distinctions exist between plants and animals, more developed and less developed species, and creatures that live in water and those living on land. Some species lay eggs, others carry their young inside their bodies, some eat plants, others are carnivorous, and some, like giant redwoods, live for centuries, while others, such as fruit flies, live for only several hours.

Polarities exist within the structure and function of each living thing. If we take the human body as an example, we see that it has a left and right side, an upper and lower portion, a front and back, an inside and outside. The twin branches of the autonomic nervous system—the sympathetic and parasympathetic—work in an antagonistic, yet complementary manner to control the body's automatic functions. The endocrine system operates in a similar way. The pancreas secretes insulin, which lowers the blood sugar level, and also secretes anti-insulin, which causes it to rise. Polarity exists at every level of biological organization. The bloodstream is counterbalanced by the lymph stream, estrogen by testosterone, DNA by RNA, red blood cells by white blood cells, growth-enhancing genes by growth-suppressing genes, activating neurotransmitters by inhibiting neurotransmitters, collagen by elastin, sodium ions by potassium ions, and so on throughout the body.

Complementary opposites exist in movement and function. Walking involves up and down, forward and backward, and left and right motions. As one leg is lifted up, the other is pushed down. As one leg moves forward, the opposite arm moves backward, and so on in a series of alternating movements. In any action, certain parts of the body are engaged in active movement, while others remain relatively still; certain parts lead, while others follow; certain muscles expand, while others contract. Periods of active movement alternate with periods of rest.

Moment to moment, we breathe in and breathe out, as the movements of the heart, lungs, and digestive organs alternate between expansion and contraction, activation and inhibition. In the morning we get up, and at night we lie down. When we speak, our voice alternates between high and low tones, rapid and slow speech, and periods of sound and silence. When we write, our hand moves up and down, we press the pen to the paper and then raise it, we begin sentences and then complete them, and move from left to right across the page. One hand holds the pen, the other supports the paper.

The rhythms of daily life—waking and sleeping, appetite and fullness, movement and rest—are animated by polarity, as are relationships between people. Some people are male, others female, some are large, others small, some are thin, others heavy, some are fair skinned, others have dark skin. Some people are intellectual, others physical, some are blonde, others brunette, some are born in the spring, others in the fall. Complementary opposites provide the basis for comparisons between people, and underlie the relationship between self and other, I and the universe, and humanity and nature. They are at the root of all perception and evaluation. All things are composed of polarities, and polarities define the relationships between things. Reality is a unified field of countless interrelationships, all of which are defined by polarity. Polarities, or complementary opposites, are a common factor unifying all of existence.

Review your life. See how it continually alternates between complementary opposites. At certain times we feel active and energetic, at others, we feel quiet and peaceful. At certain periods we feel positive, at others, negative. We experience health and sickness, success and failure, coming together and separation. These alternating patterns are not unique to human beings, but occur throughout the universe. They represent the order of nature itself.

These examples bring us to principles which express the truth of complementary opposites:

1. What has a front, has a back.

(Everything is composed of complementary opposites; all things have their opposite which is at the same time complementary. Things cannot exist without their opposite. Commonness is the reverse side of difference, and vice-versa.)

2. The bigger the front, the bigger the back.

(The more polarized something is, the more it creates its opposite.)

3. All antagonisms are complementary.

(Complementary opposites support each other; both are necessary to the whole. Unity is complementary to diversity; diversity is complementary to unity.)

Together with the four principles presented in Chapter 1, these principles comprise what in macrobiotics are referred to as the Seven Universal Principles of the Order of the Universe. These universal, common truths govern all things.

Try making a list of the complementary opposites in your environment, including the objects in your home. Complementary opposites are everywhere and in everything. They provide the foundation for existence in our relative, ever-changing world. An understanding of complementary/opposites is essential for world peace. The knowledge that all antagonisms are complementary can lead humanity beyond struggle and toward all-embracing unity.

Chapter Three
Yin and Yang

In the beginning, God created the heaven and the earth.
—Genesis, Chapter 1

If we consider the complementary opposites in ourselves and the world around us, we notice certain correspondences between them. These correspondences make it possible to categorize them in a consistent manner. Using the earth as our common frame of reference, let us evaluate the polarity existing between up and down and horizontal and vertical.

Movement in an upward direction means movement away from the earth, while downward movement implies movement toward the earth. (The distinction between up and down exists only in relation to physical bodies, such as stars and planets. There is no "up" or "down" in space.) If something has a vertical form, a greater portion of its mass extends upward away from the earth, while if something has a horizontal form, a greater portion of its mass lies closer to the earth. Upward movement gives rise to vertical forms, while downward movement gives rise to horizontal forms.

If we view the earth from a distance, we see that the center of the earth corresponds to the inside, while the surface or periphery corresponds to the outside. Downward movement means movement in an inward direction toward the center of the earth, while upward movement implies movement in an outward direction away from the center and toward the periphery. Thus we can link these pairs of opposites as follows:

upward movement (up)	downward movement (down)
vertical	horizontal
outward movement	inward movement
periphery (outside)	center (inside)

When something expands, it increases in size, and when it contracts, it becomes smaller. Largeness is a property of expansion, and smallness a property of contraction. If we relate these attributes to position, expanding force tends to push things toward the outside or periphery, while contracting force causes things to gather toward the center. Upward movement is actually outward or expanding motion away from the earth, while downward movement is actually a form of contracting motion toward the earth. Largeness and expansion are therefore consistent with the characteristics in the left-hand column, while smallness and contraction are consistent with those in the right-hand column. If we add these new attributes to our list, our classification is as follows (for convenience, the attributes on the left are listed as "alpha" and those on the right as "omega," using the Greek terms that denote complementary opposites):

Alpha	Omega
upward movement (up)	downward movement (down)
vertical	horizontal
outward movement	inward movement
periphery (outside)	center (inside)
large	small
expansion	contraction

Now that expansion and contraction have been added to our list, it is easy to place other complementary attributes in either category. When things absorb water, for example, they expand and become larger, and when they dry out, they contract and shrink. Wetness can be included under alpha, and dryness under omega. As things expand, they become lighter and less dense, and when they contract, they become increasingly dense and heavy. Density and heaviness can thus be grouped under omega, while lightness can be classified under alpha. Because solids are dense and heavy in comparison to liquids or gases, we would classify them under omega. Liquids and gases are lighter and more diffuse, and are thus classified under alpha.

Heat is a property of contracting force or movement, while cold is a property of expansion. Space, which is infinitely expanded, is cold, while heat is a product of highly condensed stars and planets. Contact produces heat; separation produces coldness. Space is also dark. Brightness is a characteristic of condensed points known as stars. Heat and brightness can be classified under omega, while coldness and darkness match the characteristics under alpha.

The complementary opposites that comprise reality are actually appearances of two primal forces. Attributes such as temperature, size, weight, structure, form, position, and wavelength yield numerous complementary tendencies that display a stronger tendency either toward expansive force, or toward contractive force.

Thousands of years ago in China, these primal forces were given the names yin and yang. The term *yin* refers to the primal force of expansion (centrifugal force) found throughout the universe, and corresponds to the attributes listed in the alpha column. The term *yang* refers to the primal force of contraction (centripetal force) found throughout the universe, and corresponds to the attributes listed under omega. Although the terms yin and yang were first used in China, an understanding of complementary opposites is not limited to Oriental countries. A similar idea can be found in many cultures throughout the world.

In the table below, we classify a variety of complementary attributes into yin and yang. There are many ways to classify things into complementary categories, and this chart represents only one way based on the definition of yin and yang established above. Yin and yang are not absolute, if anything, they are absolutely relative. All things are composed of both, so nothing is entirely yin or entirely yang. Things are not yin or yang of themselves, but only in relation to other things.

As they are in the Book of Genesis, yin and yang can be expressed by using the terms *heaven* and *earth*. Heaven is yin or expanded, while the earth is relatively tiny, compact, and yang. However, even though its form is yin, heaven generates contracting spirals, similar to the way that cold (also yin) causes things to contract. Contracting spirals become more and more condensed. As they make the transition from energy to matter, they give rise to preatomic particles and atoms, creating stars, planets, and other material objects. Heaven's energy appears on our planet as a contractive, centripetal, downward force (yang). Heaven's force causes the earth to rotate. Meanwhile, because the earth rotates, it gives off a stream of expansive, centrifugal, upward force (yin). Earth's force creates energy that expands upward and outward, moving back toward heaven. We exist as the balancing point between these two primal energies.

Our depiction of heaven's force as yang and earth's force as yin is the same as that found in The Yellow Emperor's Classic of Internal Medicine. This classic Chinese text was composed thousands of years ago. It provided the foundation for Chinese medicine. In it the sky or heaven is described as yang, while the earth is described as yin. An identical depiction appears in the I Ching, or Book of Changes, the ancient Chinese text on the order of the universe and human destiny.

Examples of Yin and Yang

	YIN	YANG
Attribute	Centrifugal force	Centripetal force
Tendency	Expansion	Contraction
Function	Diffusion	Fusion
	Dispersion	Assimilation
	Separation	Gathering
	Decomposition	Organization
Movement	More inactive, slower	More active, faster
Vibration	Shorter wave and higher frequency	Longer wave and lower frequency
Direction	Ascent and vertical	Descent and horizontal
Position	Outward, peripheral	Inward and central
Weight	Lighter	Heavier
Temperature	Colder	Hotter
Light	Darker	Brighter
Humidity	Wetter	Drier
Density	Thinner	Thicker
Size	Larger	Smaller
Shape	More expansive, fragile	More contractive, harder
Form	Longer	Shorter
Texture	Softer	Harder
Atomic particle	Electron	Proton
Elements	N, O, P, Ca, etc.	H, C, Na, As, Mg, etc.
Environment		
Climatic effects	Tropical climate	Colder climate
Biological	More vegetable quality	More animal quality
Sex	Female	Male
Organ structure	More hollow, expansive	Compacted, condensed
Nerves	More peripheral, orthosympathetic	More central, parasympathetic
Attitude, emotion	More gentle, negative, defensive	More active, positive, aggressive
Work	More psychological, mental	More physical, social
Consciousness	More universal	More specific
Mental function	Dealing more with the future	Dealing more with the past
Culture	More spiritually oriented	More materially oriented
Dimension	Space	Time

However, we must always remember that yin and yang are relative. What is yin from one point of view may be yang from another, and vice-versa. As we can see, how we label things depends on what criteria we use.

The study of yin and yang encourages us to become broad-minded and flexible; to view life from a holistic perspective. There is no fixed interpretation of these eternal, yet ever-changing laws. Yin and yang enable us to see both sides of any issue and appreciate and embrace opposite points of view. The unifying principle of yin and yang can guide humanity toward harmony and peace.

Chapter Four
Yin and Yang
Endlessly Subdivide

Tao produces One.
One produces Two.
Two produce Three.
Three produce all things.
—Lao Tsu

From the one come two, and from two come the many. Let us
turn to the human body as an example. The upper regions of the
body are yin, while the lower regions are yang. Yet each region is
made up of yin and yang in the form of soft and hard parts, peripheral and central regions, expanded and contracted organs. Two complementary streams of bodily fluid—the bloodstream (yang) and the
lymph stream (yin)— circulate through both regions. Blood is composed of formed elements, which are yang or solid, and yin liquid or
plasma. The formed elements include red blood cells, which are yang
or compact, and white blood cells, which are yin or expanded.

Red blood cells are made up of both yin and yang. Each cell contains a yin cell membrane and a yang cell body, and is composed of
hemoglobin, a yang protein containing iron, and yin phospholipids.
(Hemoglobin comprises 60 to 80 percent of the solid portion of the
cell; therefore, red blood cells are on the whole yang.) Hemoglobin is
itself composed of a yang iron-containing portion (hematin), and a
yin simple protein (globin).

All things in a given category can be arranged in a continuum, or
spectrum, that appears between the primal forces of yin and yang.
Any given category of things can be related to other categories and to
the environment as a whole according to yin and yang. Our environment on earth offers a clear example of a yin-yang spectrum. Below
we arrange the key features of the earth and its environment in a

spectrum from yang (most condensed) to yin (most expanded):

Yang   **Yin**
Core   Mantle   Crust   Water   Air   Ions   Vibration

The color spectrum offers another example of this principle. Clear light polarizes into the seven colors of the spectrum, and these can be classified from yang (long wave) to yin (short wave):

Yang   **Yin**
Red   Orange   Brown   Yellow   Green   Blue   Violet

Yin and yang exist at every level of life, from the macrocosmic to the microcosmic, within our outer and inner environments. Human beings exist as a yang, contracted center within the yin, expanded environment of the earth. However, the earth is part of a much larger unit, the solar system, and is yang or compact in relation to this expanded outer environment. The solar system is, in turn, compact and tiny in relation to the Milky Way. And, as large as it is, the galaxy is actually a infinitesimally small point within the universe as a whole.

Our internal environment is structured in a similar way. Organs are dense and compact (yang) in relation to the environment of the body as a whole (yin). Each organ, in turn, provides the expanded environment for billions of tiny cells. Each cell, in turn, serves as the expanded environment for the nucleus, while the nucleus serves as the expanded environment for DNA and RNA. Each strand of DNA is a macrocosmic environment for individual molecules of protein and carbohydrate, and these are yin in relation to individual atoms. Atoms, which are composed largely of empty space, provide the yin, expanded environment within which preatomic particles, such as protons and electrons, exist.

Inner and outer, above and below, macrocosm and microcosm. Everywhere we look we find yin and yang.

Chapter Five
Opposites Attract

You are the yin to my yang
The yang to my yin.
From the depth of my soul,
I thank you for loving me
As I love you.
> —Becket, Massachusetts, September 1999

Yin and yang are not static, but always changing. Everything is constantly in motion. Motion and change are governed by the attraction of opposites. Yin attracts yang, and yang attracts yin. The attraction of opposites occurs everywhere, at all levels of life. It is the underlying force that animates life itself.

Atoms are formed by the attraction between protons and electrons, or the attraction existing between plus and minus. A similar attraction causes atoms to combine and form molecules. Common salt offers a good example. Sodium is yang or contractive, while chlorine is yin or expansive. They are strongly polarized, and therefore strongly attracted. When they combine, sodium atoms become even more yang by giving up an electron (yin) to an atom of chlorine, causing the chlorine atom to become even more yin. The sodium atoms then take on a positive charge, while the chlorine atoms become negatively charged. These oppositely charged atoms, or ions, bond with tremendous force, forming stable molecules of salt.

In each molecule of water, two atoms of hydrogen (yang) share electrons with an atom of oxygen (yin). These polarized molecules link up with other molecules when the positively charged hydrogen nuclei of one molecule link up with the negatively charged electrons in the oxygen atom of a neighboring molecule. These hydrogen bonds are strong and are responsible for the tight cohesiveness of water.

DNA, the basic building block of life, is formed through the bonding and building up of basic organic compounds that occur because of mutual attraction. DNA is constructed of four nucleotide bases: adenosine, thymidine, guanine, and cytosine. Just like the positive and negative poles of a magnet, these bases bond into pairs because of mutual affinity. Thymidine is especially complementary to adenosine, and always pairs with it. Guanine is strongly polarized with cytosine, and always links up with it. Each strand of DNA is held together by hydrogen bonds existing between the bases.

Hormones secreted by the endocrine glands circulate freely throughout the bloodstream, yet only affect specific "target" organs. These effects are due to the attraction of opposites. The attraction between hormone and receptor is highly specific: the molecules of a particular hormone match receptors on the cells of its "target" organ in the way that a key fits a lock. If a hormone does not match a particular receptor, it continues circulating until it finds the receptor that complements it most perfectly. Hormones are either yin or yang, activating or inhibiting. Adrenalin, yang hormone, binds only with the yin receptors that specifically match it.

Human appetites are based on the attraction of opposites. When we are hungry, we are attracted to food; when active, we are attracted to rest; when lonely, we are attracted to companionship; when stressed, we are attracted to relaxation; and when overworked, we are attracted to leisure. Sex offers a dynamic expression of this principle. Men and women have opposite energies; men receive a stronger charge of heaven's downward force, and women, a stronger charge of earth's rising energy. Estrogen, the primary female hormone is yin. It produces the softer and more expansive female form. Testosterone, the male hormone, is yang. It cause the male body to develop a more compact form. The attraction between heaven's force (yang) and earth's force (yin) is the invisible force behind love and sexuality. Love is another word for the attraction of opposites.

Reproductive cells—the egg and sperm—are strongly polarized and strongly attracted. Even though women are on the whole more yin than men, the human ovum is concentrated and strongly yang. Sperm are created through a process of differentiation and are strongly yin. (Only one egg is released at a time; several hundred million sperm are discharged in one ejaculation.) The egg and sperm are so strongly polarized that their union results in more than just a simple combination, in which two opposites join but retain their separate identities. The union of egg and sperm results in a complete fusion in which both lose their individual identities and merge into an entirely new being that blends the qualities of both into one.

The attraction of opposites produces dramatic new results. When egg and sperm unite, they begin a creative process that results in a new human being. When a man and a woman unite in love, their unity transcends the individuality of each. When oxygen combines with hydrogen, these two elements create a new substance—water—that bears little resemblance to the invisible gases that create it. When yin and yang unite, yin becomes less yin and yang becomes less yang. The degree of attraction depends on the degree of polarity. The more strongly polarized things are, the more strongly they are attracted, and the more they change once they unite with their opposite.

The attraction of opposites is universal. Love is universal. It is the invisible force that animates the whole universe. A popular song once stated, "love makes the world go 'round." These words reveal a universal truth.

Chapter Six
Likes Repel

*Attraction and falling in love are love, but repulsion and
separation are also love.*
—Michio Kushi

Just as opposites attract, likes repel. Yin repels yin; yang repels
yang. The force of attraction is yang; it represents coming together of
opposites. The force of repulsion is yin; it results in the separation or
coming apart of likes. Two positive poles repel each other, as do two
negative poles. Bright colors, which are yang, reflect sunlight, while
yin dark colors absorb it. Animals, which are yang in relation to
plants, breathe in oxygen, a yin gas, while breathing out yang carbon
dioxide. Being yin, plants perform the opposite function: they absorb
carbon dioxide and repel oxygen.

The movement of heat follows the same pattern. Heat is repelled
by itself: it flows from hotter objects to colder ones. Moreover, substances that are yang have a greater resistance to heat (also yang)
than yin substances. Metals, which are solid and yang, have higher
melting temperatures than yin liquids or gases.

When you boil an egg, heat, which is yang, is readily attracted to
the egg white, which is yin. Heat is less attracted to the yolk, which is
also yang. The white of the egg thus cooks more rapidly than the
yolk. In order to overcome the natural resistance of the yolk (yang) to
heat (yang), you must add another yang factor. When you boil the
egg for more than three minutes, time (yang), plus heat (yang),
creates a doubly yang influence that overcomes the yolk's resistance.
Relative to this much stronger yang influence, the yolk becomes yin.
Its resistance breaks down and the heat penetrates and cooks it. As
long as two likes are equally matched, friction or resistance occurs.
When one becomes much stronger, resistance is overcome and replaced by attraction. We can state this another way: large yang attracts small yang; large yin attracts small yin.

Hammering a nail into wood offers another example. Physical objects are condensed, solid, and yang. By themselves, the nail and wood repel one another. No two objects can occupy the same space. In order to overcome this natural resistance, and drive the nail into the wood, we must increase the yang power of the nail. Hammering accomplishes this. When we strike the nail with a hammer, we concentrate force (yang) to a condensed point at the tip of the nail (yang.) The wood thus becomes yin in relation to the nail and accepts it. With each strike of the hammer (yang), the nail is driven deeper into the wood.

War offers a tragic example of the repulsion of likes. War can be either physical (yang) or ideological (yin.) In the case of physical conflict, opposing armies (yang) are attracted to the same goal, usually territory or space (yin.) Since both cannot occupy the same space, they clash (yang repels yang.) The conflict continues as long as both sides are equally matched. However, if one side is stronger (yang), the other side becomes yin in relation to it. At that point, the weaker side surrenders (yin). The resulting harmony between yin and yang causes the conflict to cease and peace to be restored.

Attraction and repulsion operate at the microscopic level. The body's immune response is animated by the polarity between self and non-self. Immune cells are attracted to substances that are "non-self," and aim at neutralizing the polarity these substances have with the body's cells. When yang antibodies coat a yin virus, they reverse the polarity of its receptors, causing it to become more yang. As a result, rather than being attracted to the body's cells, which are also yang, the virus is repelled. The reversal of polarity renders the virus inactive by interfering with its ability to bind with cells.

Attraction and repulsion are influenced by time. Once opposites bond, they start to change. They become more like each other. Once men and women marry, the husband tends to become yin or domestic, while the wife becomes yang or assertive. They take on characteristics of the other. Over time, the polarity that brought them together becomes less intense. Sex illustrates this clearly. A man and a woman cannot continue having sex indefinitely. They need to take a break in order to recharge their energies. Separation allows a man to regain his masculinity and a woman her femininity. After a period of separation, they are again attracted to one another.

Parents and children are attracted to each other because of the strong polarity existing between them, and are united by bonds of love and affection. However, as children grow, they become more like their parents and the natural attraction between parents and children becomes less, often changing to repulsion. That is why grown children leave home and seek an independent life in the outside world.

Whenever we are attracted to something, we are at the same time repelled (or less attracted) by something else. Whatever it is we seek, be it food, health, rest, companionship, adventure, or success, is making balance with our present condition. We are attracted to what we lack, and are repelled by what we have. When we are hungry, we eat, and when we are full, we stop eating. If we are active, we are attracted to rest. After a period of rest, we seek new activity. Attraction and repulsion continuously alternate, creating perpetual cycles of movement and change. Yin changes into yang, and yang changes into yin. The alternating pulse exists everywhere, from the life cycle of cells to the life cycle of galaxies, and from the rhythm of the tides to the rhythm of the heart.

Chapter Seven
Extremes Change Into
Their Opposites

But many that are first shall be last; and the last shall be first.
—St. Matthew, Chapter 19

Once an article appeared in the press that examined the lives of people who had each won a million dollars in the lottery. In each case, this sudden good fortune led to a series of disasters, tragedies, and ultimately unhappiness. Each of the winners stated that he or she was much happier before winning the lottery. Experiences such as these show that good fortune and bad fortune are essentially relative. Also, when things become extreme in any direction, they tend to change into their opposite. (These experiences are also examples of "what has a front has a back," and "the bigger the front, the bigger the back.")

On the earth, heaven's yang energy produces centripetal force, contraction, inward motion, density, pressure, mass, and solidity. Upon reaching its extreme point, it gives rise to heat. Heat, in turn produces yin in the form of centrifugal force, expansion, outward motion, less density, lack of pressure, decomposition, and diffusion. Ultimately, it gives rise to cold, which in turn causes contraction. At the extremity, yin changes into yang and yang changes into yin.

Water offers a perfect example. At any moment, water exists in a variety of forms. Think of the placid stillness of a pond and compare that to the active rush of water down a mountain stream. Then consider ice crystals, and compare them to invisible molecules of water vapor. In all of these appearances, we are still talking about the same substance—water.

Water in its various forms is not static. It is constantly moving and changing. Water is like a phantom that appears and disappears. One moment you see it, and in the next, you do not. In one incarnation, it may appear calm and peaceful; in the next, turbulent and powerful.

In all of its forms and changes, water follows the movement of yin and yang. It cycles between the opposite poles of expansion (water vapor) and contraction (ground water and ice), or between upward and downward movement. These movements are typical of cycles found everywhere.

The movement of the earth around the sun follows the same pattern. The earth's revolution gives rise to two polar opposites—winter, which is cold, dark, and yin, and summer, which is bright, hot, and yang. Yin and yang then divide so that four seasons are produced. Spring is the early stage of summer (large yang), and we can label it small or young yang. Autumn is the early stage of winter (large yin), and we can call it small or young yin. Small yang eventually develops into large yang, and small yin becomes large yin.

Each season divides into an early and late stage, such as early summer and late summer. These subdivisions yield a total of eight stages in the yearly cycle. The point at which seasonal energy changes from yin to yang and yang to yin occurs at the Solstice. At the Winter Solstice, yin reaches its peak and begins changing back toward yang. Days become longer and nights become shorter. At the Summer Solstice, yang reaches its peak and starts to change back toward yin. Days become shorter and nights become longer.

The daily cycle offers another example. The greatest polarity in the daily cycle is that between night (large yin) and day (large yang). Morning represents the early stage of day and corresponds to small yang. Evening is the early stage of night, and represents small yin. These four stages then divide into two—early and late—and produce eight stages in the daily cycle. It is not until yin reaches a peak in deep night that energy begins to move in the opposite direction. (The darkest hour is just before dawn.) It is not until mid-day (great yang) that energy changes back toward yin.

These cycles show how yin and yang subdivide. In both cycles, one movement (e.g., the revolution of the earth around the sun or the rotation of the earth on its axis) gives rise to a cycle based on the alternation between polarized opposites. These opposite poles divide into two, and each of these divides into two. This process occurs in the dimension of space as well as in the dimension of time, giving rise to the cardinal directions.

In the spatial realm, one universe divides into two polar opposites, which we label North (large yin) and South (large yang.) West, the direction of sunset, corresponds to small yin, while East, the direction of sunrise, corresponds to small yang, yielding four cardinal directions. Each of the four cardinal directions then divides again into Northeast, Southeast, Southwest, and Northwest, producing the eight cardinal directions.

An understanding of this process lies at the heart of Oriental cosmologies, including those of Buddhism and the I Ching. The I Ching explains the universal process of change in sixty-four stages. In the I Ching, the eight stages described above are divided again, yielding sixteen stages, and again, yielding thirty-two stages, and once again, producing sixty-four clearly defined stages of change. Each stage is represented by a symbol, or hexagram, made up of six lines. The hexagram for heaven (great yang) is represented by six solid lines. The hexagram for earth (great yin) is composed of six divided lines. The remaining sixty-two hexagrams are composed of varying combinations of both solid and divided lines, and represent all the possible combinations that exist between great yang and great yin. Each hexagram has a specific interpretation (many of which were written by Confucius), and each is given a descriptive name, such as "the Creative," or "the Receptive."

By consulting the I Ching, a person can determine at which stage in the universal cycle a specific undertaking or event is situated. He or she can also gain insight into how a specific situation might change in the future.

Western thinkers, including those of ancient Greece, were aware that the natural world, including the world of human affairs, was governed by cosmic cycles. The goddess Fortune was depicted as turning a huge cosmic wheel, the "wheel of fortune." The Greeks believed cosmic cycles governed human destiny. The ancient view of time was cyclic, not linear. Modern science has replaced the cyclic view of time with the notion of time as a linear. Science assumes the universe began at some fixed point, such as the "big bang," rather than seeing the process of creation, destruction, and new creation as a repeating cycle. In reality, the flow of time is neither circular nor linear. Time unfolds in the form of a spiral. The spiral model explains why things are always new and fresh, yet change according to a repeating pattern. Every day is a new day; yet the pattern of day and night remains the same. Every year is a new year; yet the changing of the seasons continues year in and year out.

This alternating rhythm is found everywhere; from the waxing and waning of the moon to the changing of the seasons. Our lives are no exception. Attraction changes into repulsion; repulsion gives way to fresh new attraction. We can only eat so much meat before we lose our appetite for animal food and become vegetarian. We can only pursue material wealth for so long before we lose interest and start to seek spiritual development. (Conversely, our pursuit of spiritual development can continue for only so long before we begin seeking material security.) We can only tolerate so much physical exertion before we collapse from exhaustion. Everything has a limit. Every action has an opposite reaction. Opposites attract. What we seek, we become. All things eventually change into their opposites.

Chapter Eight
The Five Transformations

For you have five trees in Paradise which are
unmoved in summer or in winter and their leaves
do not fall. Whoever knows them will not taste
death.
     —The Gospel According to Thomas

The changing of the seasons provides a familiar example of a universal cycle. In the spring, planetary energy reawakens. Plants grow, buds and leaves appear on trees, and flowers blossom. Animals become active; for many, spring is the annual mating season. Frogs begin chirping, and robins and other birds return from the tropics to their northern habitats. People spend time outdoors, doing yard work, spring cleaning, and enjoying the sunshine and warm weather. Farmers plant their crops, and families plant their gardens. Baseball, a more yin, warm weather sport, begins its season. Easter, the spring celebration of Christianity, commemorates resurrection and rebirth. These changes are examples of upward expansive energy. In Oriental philosophy, this stage of energy is referred to as "tree nature."

Energy continues in a yin direction during the spring. It reaches a peak in summer. The plant and animal kingdoms are fully alive. Vegetation that was dormant in winter is now in full bloom. Seeds planted in spring now yield mature plants. Birds, animals, and insects are fully active, and lush growth dominates the landscape. As days become longer and nights shorter, people spend a lot of time outdoors. Summer is the time of vacation and relaxation. People are attracted to the water (yin), and swim and water ski, both of which require buoyancy (yin.) They attend open air concerts and eat outdoors at picnics. The Fourth of July, that quintessential American summer holiday, centers around fireworks launched into the night sky which burst into streams of light and color. In Oriental philosophy, this stage of highly expansive, active energy is known as "fire nature."

Once it reaches the peak of expansion, planetary energy begins to move in the opposite direction. Energy starts to move downward and inward. This occurs during the period known as late summer. Plants become drier and more contracted, as the growth of summer comes to an end. Leaves change from green (yin) to yellow, brown, and red (yang.) Crickets appear and their song heralds the end of summer. Squirrels gather acorns in preparation for the coming winter. Farmers get ready to harvest their crops, children return to school, and people become busier and more serious than they were during the summer. Football, a more yang cold weather sport, begins its season. In Oriental philosophy, the stage of downward energy represented by late summer is known as "soil nature."

The process of contraction continues through the autumn, reaching a peak at the Winter Solstice. During this time, farmers gather the autumn harvest, grass and other plants become brown and dry, leaves dry up and fall to the ground. Trees appear contracted and bare. Plants store energy below ground deep within their roots. Insects disappear, birds fly south, and animals go into hibernation. Ponds and lakes freeze over. Days become shorter, nights longer. People huddle indoors before a fire and drink hot cider. Ice hockey, a very yang winter sport, begins its season. Autumn is the season of harvest celebrations, symbolized by North American Thanksgiving, during which time families gather to share food and give thanks. At the time of the Solstice, when contracting energy reaches a peak, people celebrate by staging festivals of light, including Hanukkah and Christmas. In Oriental philosophy, the contracting, gathering energy we see in autumn is referred to as "metal nature."

Following the Solstice, days become longer, and nights shorter. Energy begins moving back toward expansion. Cold temperatures offset this somewhat, so that in winter, the earth's energy tends to "float" back and forth between expansion and contraction, in the way ice floats to the top of a lake. People either stay indoors, or are attracted to the mountains where they enjoy downhill skiing and other yang pursuits. Some people seek balance by going to warmer climates. On the surface, energy appears to be dormant and frozen. However, just below the surface, energy is gathering, waiting to burst forth with the coming of spring. In Oriental philosophy, the stage of floating energy represented by winter is known as "water nature."

The procession of the seasons, so familiar to everyone in the temperate zones, is an example of an alternating cycle with five stages:

1. upward energy, or tree nature;
2. actively expanding energy, or fire nature
3. downward energy, or soil nature;

4. gathering, condensed energy, or metal nature;
5. floating energy, or water nature.

In macrobiotics, we refer to this universal cycle as the five transformations. The cycle of day and night offers another example of this
process. Morning corresponds to upward or tree energy. In the morning we get up and begin the day's activity. Noon is the time of fire
energy, and this is the most active time of day. Afternoon corresponds to downward, soil energy, evening to condensed metal energy, and night to floating water energy. At night, contracting energy
causes us to lie down and sleep, or "float away." As we have seen,
everything cycles back and forth between yin and yang, or expansion
and contraction. The five transformations is another way of understanding this universal process.

An ancient, historical reference to the five transformations can be
found in the Nei Ching, or Yellow Emperor's Classic of Internal Medicine. In this classic text, foods, organs, seasons, and other phenomena are classified according to these five stages. For thousands of
years, acupuncturists, herbal doctors, and others trained in traditional Chinese medicine have utilized the five transformations in the di-
agnosis and treatment of illness.

In the Nei Ching, bodily organs are listed in pairs, with solid and
compact organs (yang) matched with hollow and expanded ones
(yin.) The lungs and large intestine form one pair. The lungs have a
dense and compact structure (they are filled with air sacs and blood
vessels), and are classified as yang. The large intestine is a long, hollow tube, and is classified as yin. Both organs process the outer environment in the form of air, food, and water. The lungs are yang, and
process gas (yin), while the yin large intestine processes solids and
liquids (yang).

The heart and small intestine are also classified as a pair. Their
complementarity can be seen in their position—the heart is located in
the upper body, and the small intestine in the lower—and in their
structure—the heart is a compact muscle (yang) and the small intestine, an extended hollow tube (yin.) The heart and small intestine
function in a complementary manner. The small intestine is the site
where nutrients are absorbed into the bloodstream for distribution by
the heart.

The kidneys and bladder are classified as another complementary
pair. The kidneys are solid and compact (yang), and the bladder is
hollow and expanded (yin). The kidneys filter the blood and produce
urine, and the bladder is the site in which urine is stored before being
discharged.

The spleen and pancreas share blood and energy streams and in Oriental medicine, are considered as a unit. Both are complementary to the stomach. The spleen and pancreas have a dense, compact form (yang), and the stomach a hollow and expanded structure (yin.) Once again, these organs function in a complementary way; for example, the pancreas secretes yang digestive juices that complement the yin acids secreted by the stomach.

The liver and gallbladder are another complementary pair. The liver is compact (yang), and the gallbladder is a hollow sac (yin). The liver secretes bile. The gallbladder stores bile and discharges it into the small intestine.

Each pair of organs corresponds to a stage in the five transformations. The liver and gallbladder are examples of upward/tree energy; the heart and small intestine, active/fire energy; the spleen, pancreas, and stomach, downward/soil energy; the lungs and large intestine, condensed/metal energy; and the kidneys and bladder, floating/water energy. This classification was first recorded in the Yellow Emperor's Classic of Internal Medicine. However, the Yellow Emperor's Classic omits any explanation of why the organs are classified in this manner. The key to why the organs are classified as such can be found in understanding the way in which the energies of yin and yang appear in the body. In his seminars, macrobiotic educator Michio Kushi explains this connection quite clearly.

Upward energy, or earth's force, is stronger on the right side of the body. Downward energy, or heaven's force, is stronger on the left. We can see the predominance of upward/earth's force in the ascending colon and the functions of the right hemisphere of the brain. The right hemisphere is the source of yin artistic thinking. The predominance of downward/heaven's force is seen in the descending colon and the functions of the brain's left hemisphere. The left hemisphere is where yang analytical thinking is produced.

Upward/earth's force nourishes the liver and gallbladder. Downward/heaven's force nourishes the spleen/pancreas and stomach. Compare the structure and functions of the liver (right side) and the pancreas (left side.) The liver is a large organ that expands upward like a tree with many branches. The pancreas is smaller, flatter, and positioned lower in the body. When the liver is active, it releases glycogen into the bloodstream. Glycogen is converted into glucose, raising the level of blood sugar and producing a surge of energy. When the pancreas is active, it releases insulin. This yang hormone has the opposite effect. It lowers blood sugar and stabilizes the body's energy. The liver and gallbladder are classified in the upward/tree category, while the spleen (also on the left side), pancreas, and stomach

Five Stages of Energy Transformation

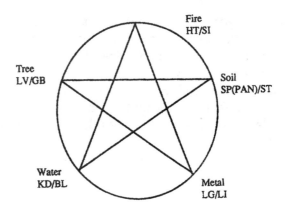

(which arches toward the left) are classified in the downward/soil category.

Running through the center of the body is an invisible energy core. Uniting the primal forces of heaven and earth, this highly charged core is the source of the body's life energy. It is along this primary channel that we find seven highly charged centers known as chakras. Energy continually radiates outward from this central core to the periphery of the body, along meridians or energy channels. The meridians branch inward, giving rise to smaller and smaller sub-divisions. At the end of each subdivision is a living cell. Each cell is animated by the life energy it receives through these channels. The source of life energy is the body's energy core and chakras, and these are animated by cosmic energy. Each cell is directly charged by cosmic forces, as well as by energy in the form of nourishment received through the bloodstream. This stream of energy originates with the foods produced by the earth.

Heaven and earth charge the body in an alternating pulse. Expanding and contracting rhythms animate all of the body's functions, from organ/systems to cells. Nowhere is this seen more clearly than in the expansion and contraction of the heart, an organ positioned in the region of the highly charged heart chakra. The heart's position to the left of the central core enables it to receive a strong charge of downward/heaven's force. It is this force that enables it to contract with such power.

The pulse of life is also reflected in the movements of the small intestine. The small intestine is the site where nutrients are absorbed through the microscopic villi that coat its inner lining. From here they are eventually disbursed to all of the body's cells. The villi continually expand and contract, and move from side to side. At the center of the small intestine is a highly charged energy center that animates all of these functions.

The heart and small intestine are classified in the active/fire energy category. Both organs receive energy directly from the body's central energy core. It is from this central core that life energy radiates outward to the entire body. The very active functions of the heart and small intestine reflect the highly energized state of active/fire energy.

The lungs and large intestine are classified in the condensed/metal category. The lungs are densely packed with air sacs and blood vessels. When they expand, they attract oxygen, which is yin. When they contract, they squeeze out and expel carbon dioxide, which is yang. In the lower body, the ascending colon extends upward on the right side. The transverse colon extends laterally, and the descending colon extends down the left side. The large intestine is about 1.5 meters in length, yet it is condensed by the forces of heaven and earth into a much smaller space.

The kidneys are positioned in the middle of the body toward the back. The right kidney is charged by earth's rising force, the left, by heaven's descending energy. The kidneys balance or "float" between the forces of heaven and earth, and are classified in the floating/water energy category, along with their complementary organ, the bladder.

Yin and yang and the five transformations govern our inner and outer environments. Food is the bridge between the two. Every day, we take in the condensed essence of the environment in the form of food. We use food to create our internal environment. Foods are the product of the same cycles that govern our inner and outer environments. If we select food wisely, our diet can help us achieve harmony with the environment. If our food choices are unwise, our diet causes us to lose harmony with the environment.

From the beginning, cereal grains and beans have been humanity's principal foods. They match our long and convoluted digestive tract and the structure of our teeth, the majority of which are constructed for crushing and grinding plant fibers. Until the modern age, cultures throughout the world respected human biological needs by maintaining cereal grains and soy and other beans as their primary foods. Each of these foods has a unique quality of energy, and these energies correspond to the five transformations.

Barley and wheat are classified in the upward/tree category. When ripe, these plants stand straight up. The head projects upward, with tassels extending toward heaven. Compared to other grains, barley and wheat have a light expansive quality. Adding them to brown rice produces a lighter, more fluffy dish. Barley tea cools the body and aids in the discharge of animal food. It helps dissolve hardened deposits throughout the body. Many varieties of barley and wheat are planted in the fall and harvested in spring. The energy of rye and oats is similar to that of barley and wheat, and these grains are also classified in the upward/tree category.

The expansive energy in corn is more powerful than that of barley and wheat. Corn is like a summer grass that grows tall and extends toward heaven. Corn is traditionally harvested in summer. Many varieties of corn have an expansive sweet taste. Adding it to dishes produces a light expansive quality. Corn is also popped on top of the stove until the energy of each kernel expands and bursts forth. Corn silk, the delicate hair that appears at the top of each ear of corn, is good for dissolving hardened fat and cholesterol deposits. Corn is classified in the active/fire category.

The energy of millet is opposite to that of barley and wheat. Grains of millet are yellow or red (both yang colors) and have a round shape. They are hard and tiny. When ripe, the grains bend down toward the earth. The most alkaline of the grains, millet is classified in the downward/soil category. Sweet rice, which is rounder and more glutinous than regular rice, is also classified in this category.

Rice is traditionally harvested in autumn. When ripe, the rice plant bends toward the earth. Brown rice, especially short grain rice, readily absorbs and harmonizes the energy of other grains, beans, and other foods. In macrobiotic cooking it serves as a "magnet" grain to which other foods are added. Rice is classified in the condensed/metal category.

Buckwheat is the hardest of the grains and grows easily in cold climates. It is classified in the floating/water category. In Japan, buckwheat is used to make thin noodles called soba. Soba were traditionally eaten in northern regions, while wheat noodles, called udon, were eaten in the south. Noodles made with a high percentage of buckwheat flour were traditionally eaten at New Year's during the winter/water season. Beans are also classified in the floating/water category, as are bean products such as tofu. Tofu contains a higher proportion of water than the soybeans from which it is made, and is stored in water. Tofu has a "transparent" quality that resembles water. It has little taste of its own and tends to take on the flavors of the other foods with which it is cooked.

The classification of foods according to their energetic characteristics also extends to vegetables of land and sea. Aside from providing many essential nutrients, vegetables complement the concentrated energy of grains and beans and are ideal as secondary foods in the human diet. Vegetables can be classified in the following categories:

1. upward/tree: leafy greens, including the edible tops of roots such as daikon, turnip, dandelion, and carrot, plus broccoli, cauliflower, Brussels sprouts, scallion, and chive;
2. expansive/fire: expanded leafy greens, such as collard greens, mustard greens, and Chinese cabbage, in which the root portion is generally not eaten, plus summer vegetables such as cucumber, celery, and summer squash;
3. downward/soil: vegetables with a more contracted round shape such as squash, pumpkin, cabbage, and onion;
4. condensed/metal: root vegetables such as carrot, burdock, turnip, daikon, dandelion, and lotus;
5. floating/water: edible sea vegetables such as wakame, nori, hiziki, agar, sea palm, and others.

Cooking changes the energy of food. It alters the way food affects us. Through cooking, we can adjust the energy of food to make it more yin or more yang. Cooking for a short time over a high flame activates and releases energy. Cooking for a longer time over a low flame concentrates energy. These opposite approaches give rise to five categories of cooking that correspond to the five transformations.

Upward/tree energy is accelerated by quick steaming. Steam is produced by the boiling of water, and moves in an upward direction. Leafy greens are charged by upward energy, and are often cooked this way. Pickling involves the breakdown and release of energy through fermentation. Pickling, especially quick-pickling, is classified in the upward/tree category.

Blanching, quick-sauteing, stir-frying, and deep-frying utilize intense heat and energy. Foods are exposed to a high flame for short periods of time. These methods classified in the active/fire category. When foods are cooked this way, they become strongly energized.

In contrast to these energy-activating methods are cooking styles that utilize a lower flame and longer cooking times. Stew is an example, as are the methods used to boil whole grains. In stew, grains, beans, vegetables, and other foods are slowly cooked until they are thoroughly blended. When whole grains are boiled, they are cooked over a slow flame with a lid on the pot. These cooking methods concentrate energy and are classified in the downward/soil category.

Pressure cooking is a concentrated form of boiling. Grains, beans, and other foods are boiled in a tightly sealed pot under pressure (yang.) Pressure cooking is classified in the condensed/metal category. Baking and broiling cause foods to become drier and harder. Baking takes place in a yang, enclosed space (an oven), and causes food to have a drying and tightening effect on the body. These methods produce strong contractive effects and are also classified in the condensed/metal category.

In between cooking styles that activate or concentrate energy is another method that incorporates aspects of both. In this method, foods are cooked in plenty of water. This method is known as soup. By adjusting ingredients and cooking times, soups can be made to produce lighter, more expansive effects, or heavier, more concentrated effects. Soup is classified in the floating/water category.

Health is the state in which our inner environment changes in accord with the cycles of our planetary environment. Our planetary environment is vastly larger and more powerful than we are as individuals. The planetary environment does not need to adapt to us; our task is to adapt to it. Every day, we wake up in the morning, become active, and rest at night. If we oppose this cycle by sleeping during the day and being active at night, we eventually become sick. We can only resist the rotation of the earth for so long before our energy becomes depleted and we lose our health. Sickness is the state in which the microcosm opposes the macrocosm.

The recovery of health is the process in which we bring our microcosm into alignment with the environment. This can be accomplished in a number of ways, for example, by resting when we are exhausted, by adjusting our thinking and lifestyle to achieve greater harmony with our surroundings, and by adjusting our diet to make balance with our environment.

Yin and yang and the five transformations unify humanity and nature. They are the basis for a truly holistic approach to living on planet earth. Health and healing originate in the concept of wholeness. Being whole implies that we embrace and balance the complementary energies of yin and yang, including the stages of energy which they produce. Food is the bridge between our inner and outer worlds. In selecting foods for health, it is essential that we balance yin and yang by incorporating foods that correspond to each of the five stages. Variety in food selection and cooking methods is the practical means to achieve such comprehensive balance. It is also important to be mindful of seasonal and daily changes, and to adjust our cooking and selection of foods to harmonize with them.

An understanding of how foods reflect the energy of the environment and how they interact with the energy of the body enables us to apply certain foods and cooking methods to strengthen bodily organs and functions by emphasizing the foods of a certain transformation in order to nourish the organs of that transformation. It also enables us to offset symptoms, by applying foods and remedies with energies that are opposite to those of the symptom. Yin and yang and the five transformations are the key to the use of food in health and healing. They provide the basis for an energy medicine capable of guiding humanity toward genuine health and peace.

Chapter Nine
Making Balance

Macrobiotics is humanity's universal common dream. It is as free and accessible as air, water, and sunlight. It will continue as long as there is a humanity on this planet.
—Becket, Massachusetts, September, 1999

Macrobiotics is the art of balancing yin and yang in our daily life so that we can successfully adapt to our ever changing environment. One of the most basic principles of macrobiotic living is to eat an ecological, environmentally-based diet. That means to rely primarily on foods native to the climate and environment in which we live. Until the modern age, people were more or less dependent on the products of their regional agriculture. Foods that grew in their area formed the basis of their daily diet. It was not until modern technology that it became possible for people to base their diets on foods from regions with far different climates.

Today, it is common for people to consume bananas from South America, sugar from the Caribbean, pineapples from the South Pacific, or kiwi from New Zealand. These foods are the product of a tropical climate. Yang, hot climates cause plants and animals to have a yin or expanded form. Yin, cold climates produce yang or contracted plant and animal life. Food from the tropics is yin; food from temperate or cold climates is yang. Our health depends on our ability to adapt to our immediate environment. When we eat foods from a climate that is different from ours, we lose that adaptability. Tropical fruits, sugar, and chocolate make people too yin to adapt successfully to a cold northern climate.

As society moved away from its traditional, ecologically-based diet, there has been a corresponding rise in chronic illness. Therefore, for optimal health, we need to return to a way of eating based on foods produced in our own bioregion, or at least on foods grown in a bioregion with a climate similar to ours.

Foods with yang, or contracted energy remain viable longer and can come from a greater distance than foods with yin, or expansive energy. Sea salt and sea vegetables are examples. They are rich in contracted minerals and can come from the oceans around the world, provided these waters are within your hemisphere. Grains, especially with the outer husk attached, remain intact for a long time, even thousands of years, and can come from anywhere in your continent. Beans also travel well and can come from a similarly wide area. However, vegetables and fruits are yin or expansive; they decompose rapidly, and unless they are naturally dried or pickled, are best taken from your immediate area.

Cooking enabled humanity to live practically anywhere on earth. Through cooking, we are able to balance our climate. Cooking also enables us to make balance with the changing of the seasons. High temperatures and bright sunshine produce a stronger charge of yin upward energy in the environment. Water evaporates more rapidly and plants become lush and expanded. During spring and summer, yin upward energy is stronger, as it is in the tropics. Then toward the end of summer, energy starts to change, moving downward and inward. In colder and darker conditions, such as those in northern climates, or during autumn and winter, yang, downward or contracting energy is stronger.

How do we adapt to these conditions? During spring and summer, we make our diet lighter and fresher, meaning that we use less fire in cooking. We do not need as much fire in our cooking because fire is already there in the form of strong sunshine. When it is hot, we do not need warmth from our food. As we move into autumn and winter, with cooler temperatures and stronger downward energy, we make our food hearty and warming by using more fire in cooking. Similarly, lighter cooking and more fresh food is appropriate in a hot climate, while stronger cooking helps us make balance with a cold climate.

Day to day, atmospheric energy alternates between yin and yang. Yin upward energy is stronger in the morning, while yang downward energy is stronger in the afternoon and evening. In order to move together with this cycle, it is better to eat a light breakfast. A breakfast of eggs and bacon is extremely yang (dense and heavy), and opposes the upward energy of morning. Breakfast grains can be cooked with more water, so that they become lighter and more easily digested. Dinner can include a greater number of side dishes, and we normally eat more in the evening, since at that time, atmospheric energy is more condensed and inward-moving. Lunch can also be quick and light, since at noon, atmospheric energy is very active and expansive. Quick light cooking, such as that in which we reheat leftovers, can be done at that time.

Another important principle is to eat according to our needs as a species. Our teeth reveal the ideal balance of yin and yang in the human diet. We have thirty-two adult teeth. There are twenty molars and premolars. The word *molar* is a Latin word for *millstone,* or the stones used to crush wheat and other grains into flour. These teeth are not suited for animal food, but for crushing or grinding grains, beans, seeds, and other tough plant fibers. There are also eight front incisors (from the Latin, *to cut*) and these are well-suited for cutting vegetables. We also have four canine teeth. The canines can be used for animal food, not necessarily meat, but foods such as white-meat fish. The ideal proportion of foods as reflected in the teeth is five parts grain and other tough fibrous foods, two parts vegetables, and one part animal food. The ideal ratio between plant food (yin) and animal food (yang) is seven to one.

The modern diet does not reflect this pattern. Rather than whole grains, meat or other types of animal food are the primary foods. Vegetables are used as garnish to the main course of animal food. Cereal grains are eaten almost as an afterthought, and are eaten in the form of white bread, white rolls, and other highly refined products. Refined bread or rolls are used simply as a vehicle to carry a hot dog, hamburger, or some other type of animal food. Grains are an incidental part of the modern diet.

Today, people are eating the opposite of what they should be eating. That is why so many health problems exist in the modern world. One of the clearest messages I received from the books of George Ohsawa was that grain-based diets are superior to animal-based diets. When Ohsawa presented that idea many years ago, Western doctors and nutritionists laughed. They believed that animal protein was superior to plant protein, and that cultures in which animal protein formed the basis of the diet were more advanced than cultures that relied on grains and other plant foods.

However, that view is changing. The vanguard of modern nutrition now agrees that whole grains and other plant foods are better for our health than are animal foods. If we compare the health patterns of people who are eating plant-based diets with those who are eating animal food, the grain- and vegetable-eaters have far lower rates of chronic disease. There is an exception to this of course. If you would like to eat animal food, it would be better for you to move to the the Arctic Circle, an extremely yin environment. Then you can eat plenty of animal food (yang) to make balance. But if you live in Houston, where there is a very hot climate (yang) then it is out of order to eat plenty of yang barbecued beef. It does not fulfill our biological needs nor does it make our condition harmonious with our environment.

The practice of macrobiotics is based on the understanding of food as energy. Electrons and protons are not solid particles, but condensed packets of energy. Everything is actually energy, everything is composed of vibration. There is no unchanging or fixed substance in the universe. Therefore, macrobiotic understanding of food incorporates, but is not limited to, theories of modern nutrition. In modern nutrition, food is viewed as matter. In reality, there is an invisible quality to food (and to life itself) that cannot be measured scientifically. We perceive that invisible quality directly through our intuition.

In macrobiotics, we employ yin and yang to understand the fundamental energy of food. All foods are made up of varying degrees of these two basic forces. We use this understanding to see how food affects us in a very dynamic and practical way. By understanding food as energy, we see that it affects not only our physical condition, but our mind, emotions, and even our spirituality. These invisible aspects of life are a function of the quality of energy we manifest.

If we eat a food such as steak, which is very yang or contracted, we are naturally attracted to foods with the opposite quality of energy (opposites attract.) So we eat the steak with potatoes, alcohol, or a sugary dessert such as ice cream. All of these foods are extremely yin. In order to balance extremes, we have to add many things that we don't need. We wind up taking in excess fat, excess protein, excess carbohydrate, and excess water. Our body is constantly being challenged.

However, what happens when our main food is more balanced? If you look at a nutritional analysis of whole grains—brown rice, barley, millet, whole wheat—you discover that their ratio of minerals to protein and protein to carbohydrate approximates one to seven. Short grain brown rice comes closest to the one to seven ratio, that, nutritionally speaking, represents the balancing point between yin expansive and yang contractive energies on the planet as a whole. If you eat whole grains every day, your main foods are balanced in themselves. It is much easier to balance yin and yang in your diet as a whole. Eating whole grains as your primary food makes it much easier to maintain optimal nutritional and energetic balance.

Macrobiotics also teaches that we respect the endless diversity of individual needs. As we saw in the chapter on Commonness and Difference, although all people have certain fundamental things in common, each person is different. If we are active, we should eat a certain way for physical activity. If we are sitting behind a desk, our diet should be somewhat different. Men and women also need to eat differently. Between men and women, who can eat more animal food? Men. Who can eat more raw salad and sweets? Women. Children and adults also need to eat differently. Babies are already yang—small and contracted—so their diets need to be more yin—soft and sweet-tasting, with little or no salt. If you have eaten plenty of animal food in the past, in order to restore balance, you need to base your diet on plant foods. Or if you have a health problem caused by your past way of eating, you can emphasize foods with opposite energies in order to offset that.

What are the benefits of balancing yin and yang in our daily diet and way of life? Macrobiotic living can help us achieve health and longevity. People such as the Hunza in Kashmir, known for their good health and longevity, eat grains and vegetables as their main food. They were eating more or less a macrobiotic diet adapted to their mountainous terrain and climate. The first benefit of macrobiotic eating is health and longevity.

A second benefit is peace of mind. That peace of mind comes from the awareness that we are living and eating in harmony with the universe. We are living in harmony with the movement of energy. That is the source of inner peace. Our mind and emotions are very much conditioned by what we eat. If you feed your child plenty of sugar, what kind of mind or emotions result? Children become hyperactive or cry a lot, and become overly emotional. If we eat plenty of meat, what kind of mind and emotions are produced? We become aggressive or in the extreme, even violent. What happens when we eat plenty of nightshade vegetables such as tomatoes or potatoes? We become depressed. Incidentally, these vegetables have recently been found to contain nicotine. Nicotine is an addictive substance, and that may explain why many people find it difficult to stop eating these vegetables.

As your mind and emotions become more stable and peaceful, you naturally develop a sense of family and community. Modern values—such as competition, dog eat dog, survival of the fittest, etc.—have all arisen from a carnivorous diet. Grain-eating people develop a completely opposite view. Instead of seeing scarcity on the earth, grain-eaters realize that we live in a universe of abundance. Rather than fighting over resources, the issue becomes how to share the tremendous natural wealth on our planet. Meat-eating tends to produce isolation, something like the lone hunter or lone wolf, rather than a sense of community. Hunters such as lions and hyenas are constantly fighting with each other. Grain-eaters develop a completely opposite way of thinking based on cooperation.

Macrobiotic living can also help us gain spiritual understanding. Do you think it is easy to meditate if we eat hamburgers, or if our mind is very angry or upset, or if we are always stressed out? Or if we are eating sugar or drinking Coke all the time, so that our mind is often hyperactive and scattered, can we really stabilize and center our energy? These conditions make if very difficult to enter into deep, tranquil, and peaceful meditation. In order to allow spiritual energy to smoothly channel through us, and to use that energy, macrobiotic eating—grains and vegetables—is ideal.

All great spiritual traditions included some form of dietary discipline. In the Orient, the cooking in Buddhist and Taoist monasteries was called "cooking for spiritual development." These traditions were based on the understanding that food influences our spiritual development. By selecting the proper food, we develop our spiritual quality. In these traditions, do you think animal food was a part of their diets? No. They were completely vegetarian. However, in traditional times, vegetarian eating, especially in cooler climates, meant eating cooked brown rice, daikon and other vegetables, tofu and bean products, etc., rather than a lot of raw fruit or salad.

Finally, as we achieve good health, peace of mind, a sense of family and community, and spiritual understanding, we gain the ability to play and have a big dream or adventure in this life. Macrobiotics is based on change or transmutation. In other words, we try to gain the ability to change things into their opposite according to our free will. As George Ohsawa said, "Let us change yin into yang. Let us change yang into yin." So if we are experiencing difficulty, using macrobiotic understanding, we try to change that into pleasure or enjoyment. Or if we are experiencing sickness, we self-transform that into health. Or if the world is in danger of war, as our adventure, as our play, as our challenge, we transform that into peace. You can even gain the ability to transmute or transform any type of food into your health and vitality. In other words, you embrace your antagonist and turn it into your friend. Ultimately there are no restrictions and no enemies. The realization of total freedom, or the freedom to play endlessly in this infinite universe, is the ultimate benefit of macrobiotic living.

Chapter Ten
The Wheel and the Spiral

From the outside
To the inside
A spiral weaves its track.
From the center to the outside
It always spirals back.
Always moving, always changing
In a sea of infinity.
For everything to understand
A spiral is the key.
—The Spiral Song

Once upon a time, a long time ago, a son was born into a royal family. His mother, the queen, died soon after giving birth. His father, the king, was so distraught over the loss of his beloved wife that he vowed his newborn son would never experience any form of suffering. Following the king's wishes, the prince grew up surrounded by luxury without being exposed to the poverty, sickness, and suffering that existed outside the palace.

The prince grew into a healthy young man. He married a beautiful princess, and together they conceived a son. One day, a musician came to the palace. She sang in haunting tones of distant lands, stimulating the prince's curiosity and imagination. He asked his father if he could venture outside the palace to see the world outside.

The king, still wishing to shield his son, arranged for the prince to be the center of a parade through the town. He decreed that all aged or sick people be kept out of sight, and arranged that only healthy young people be seen by the prince. On the day of the parade, the gates of the palace opened, and the prince and his escort began winding their way through the town. Both sides of the street were lined with young people who cheered the prince and threw flowers in his path.

As the procession continued, two old men appeared on a side

street. The prince saw them and asked, "What is wrong with those men?" One of his trusted friends, who was wise in the ways of the world, answered, "They are old. Aging is the decline of the body and is something everyone must go through." The prince suddenly realized there was much more to life than what he had experienced in the palace. With a burning desire to discover the truth, he climbed down from his carriage and ran down a side street with his trusted friend close behind.

The prince came upon a several huts where the villagers were living in poverty. He asked his friend what was wrong. His friend replied, "These people are living in poverty. They often don't have enough to eat. Most of the people in the world must struggle daily just to survive." For the first time in his life, the prince was confronted with the harsh reality of human suffering. Then, from within one hut, the prince heard the sound of moaning and wailing. When he entered the hut, he saw a sick man lying on a straw mat surrounded by his family. He asked his friend what was wrong and his friend replied, "That man is suffering from sickness. Sickness is the breakdown of the body and is something everyone experiences in one form or another." Again the prince was astonished.

Continuing his journey, the prince came to a river. He came upon a sight that was even more troubling. He saw a group of people moaning and wailing. At the center of the group was a funeral pyre. The flames were consuming the body lying in the middle. The prince asked his friend what was wrong and his friend replied, "That man has died. Death is the ultimate dissolution of the body. We all die eventually. No one can escape death."

At this point, the prince was overcome with emotion. He felt as if the flames were burning away his own delusions. He felt the pain of the dead man's relatives and vowed he would never go back to his previous life. He resolved to devote himself to finding a way for humanity to escape from suffering.

That night he told his father of his desire to leave the palace. The king loved his son very much and begged him to stay. He told his son that his search was pointless. Everyone, he said, is caught in the wheel of karma, or cause and effect. No one can escape the eternal cycle of birth, suffering, death, and rebirth. That was humanity's fate. The wheel of karma turned forever.

The prince's intuition told him that his father's view was not correct: that everything changes; and that nothing, not even the wheel of karma, was static. There had to be a way for human beings to escape such a condition and achieve freedom. Late that night, while everyone in the palace was asleep, the prince bade a silent farewell to his wife and infant son and slipped away. The journey of self-discovery he was about to embark upon would change the world.

The prince joined a group of ascetics who had renounced the world and retreated to the forest. There he fasted, meditated, and performed spiritual practices. His life as an ascetic continued for a number of years until one morning, while down by a river, he overheard a conversation on a boat that was passing downstream. The conversation was between a musician and his pupil. Holding a stringed instrument, the musician said to his student, "If the strings are too tight, they will break. If they are too loose, they won't play." At that instant, the prince had a revelation about the path he would follow.

The prince realized that the path to enlightenment was found in the "middle way," between extremes of yang (too tight) and yin (too loose.) He decided to accept a bowl of brown rice offered by a young woman, and began to eat to restore his strength and vitality. He continued on his own with his meditations and spiritual practices, eventually achieving the freedom and enlightenment he was seeking. Later, the prince, whose name was Siddhartha, would become known as the Buddha, or "enlightened one."

Central to the Buddha's enlightenment was his understanding that behind the world of manifestation is the eternally non-manifest. The manifest arises from the non-manifest and is as transitory and ephemeral as a dream. To exist is to change. Change is the only constant, the one eternal fact. Change occurs in an orderly cycle, and that cycle appears not as a wheel, but as a spiral. The spiral is the one constant that governs the world of being. Being equals spiral; spiral equals being. To be is to spiral. To spiral is to be.

His insight was revolutionary. It directly challenged the view that humanity was tied to an endless cycle of birth, suffering, death, and rebirth. The spiral liberated humanity from the wheel of karma. Through correct living and thinking, human beings could advance or evolve along a spiral path that led to spiritual freedom.

All movement occurs in spirals. Yin and yang appear in the form of spirals of moving energy. Spirals are visible throughout nature, from the shape of galaxies to the formation of electrons. (Try making a list of at least twenty spiral forms in nature.) The spiral explains the genesis or creation of the universe. In the infinite ocean of the universe, beyond time and space, two opposite poles arise, which we call yin and yang. Yin and yang give birth to energy and movement, causing spirals to appear like whirlpools in a stream. These spirals wind inward, so that energy condenses into matter, giving rise to our physical universe. When a spiral reaches its condensed center, it begins to expand, eventually dissolving into the infinite ocean from which it came.

Spiral of Materialization

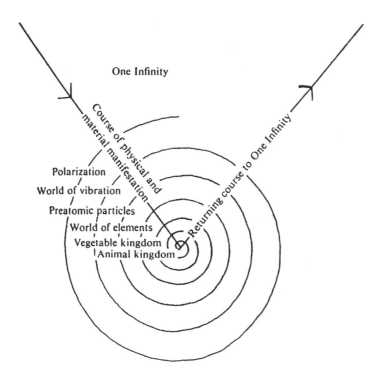

Spirals are governed by two forces: the condensing force that causes them to form (yang), and the expanding force that causes them to dissolve (yin.) Yin and yang are the origin of time and space, and time and space are the origin of our relative, ever-changing world. All things exist within the matrix of time and space, and, like the universe in which they appear, are themselves constituted as spirals. And, like the universe itself, all things follow the spiral of change and development, continually appearing (yang), disappearing (yin), and reappearing in a new form.

In macrobiotics, we call the creation of the universe "spiralgenesis." The process of spiralgenesis occurs in seven stages:

7. One infinity (the eternally non-manifest or non-being; the source of all manifestation and all being)

6. Polarization (the two primary forces that give rise to being or

manifestation)

    5. Energy (the first appearance of being; endless movement in the form of contracting and expanding spirals)

    4. Preatomic particles (condensed spirals of energy that take the form of electrons, protons, etc.)

    3. Elements (further condensed and complex spirals of energy)

    2. Plant life (further complex, self-replicating spirals of energy)

    1. Animal life, and ultimately human beings (the most condensed, complex, and free of all energy spirals)

When we view spiralgenesis from a human perspective, we can say that we attract or take in the various forms of our environment. We eat plants and elements in the form of food and water. We breathe air and absorb solar energy and other forms of light and radiation. We take in yin and yang in the form of heaven and earth's forces, and these are actually complementary expressions of one infinite force. We can also look at sprialgenesis from the opposite point of view. When we see it from the perspective of totality, it can be said that infinity changes into each of these worlds, ultimately taking human form.

The world we inhabit is the condensed form of infinity. Infinity is the expanded form of our world. Infinity moves at absolute speed, beyond space and time, yin and yang. Movement at infinite speed also equals absolute stillness. Infinity is the constant and unchanging source of the spiral, and exists both within and outside of it. The relative world is the world of spiral motion. It changes constantly and is governed by yin and yang, the unchanging order of change. Absolute and relative are not separate. One is the continuation of the other.

Infinity is the origin of our relative world. Infinity did not create our world; it changed into our world. The process of spiralgenesis, in which the large becomes small, the infinite produces relative forms, is yang. Humans are the center of that universal process, having passed through and assimilated all previous worlds. Human life represents an ending and a beginning: the conclusion of spiralgenesis and the beginning of spiralconsciousness. Like the cereal grains that are the food of their species, human beings are both the fruit and the seed of a cosmic process. Spiralconsciousness is the yin, expanding process in which a human being returns to and merges with infinity. That process continues beyond our physical life. From the human perspective, spiralgenesis is the visible front, spiralconsciousness, the invisible back.

The Buddha was spiralconscious, as were other spiritual teachers and guides. Spiralconsciousness enabled these teachers to realize their unity with God or infinity. It pointed the way toward life eternal and the development of consciousness through the worlds of matter and spirit. Spiralconsciousness opens the possibility of endless spiritual evolution, leading to absolute freedom.

In the new millennium, we have the opportunity to unite behind a common awareness of spiralgenesis, spiralconsciousness, and the order of change that governs both. Spiralawareness and yin yang consciousness can be available to everyone. The simple, yet universal, laws of change are humanity's magic carpet, Alladdin's lamp, and Holy Grail. They are the key to health, peace, and happiness in this world and all the worlds to come.

Appendix
Yin Yang Quiz

*Studying yin and yang is like trying to
hold an eel. The harder you try to grasp it,
the quicker it slips away.*
—Herman Aihara

The understanding of yin and yang is intuitive, spontaneous, and practical. The Yin Yang Quiz can help you polish your understanding of the universal laws of change. Using the principles and definitions presented in this book, try answering the following questions:

1. In comparing a stone to water, which has a yin form?

2. In comparing water to air, which has a yang form?

3. Which of the following moves in a yin direction?
   Evaporating mist –
   Falling rain

4. During which time of day is energy moving in a yang direction?
   Sunrise
   Sunset –

5. Which of the following occupies a yin position?
   Apple seeds
   The skin of an apple –

6. Which group of people is yang?
   A team playing a game –
   The spectators watching them

7. Which activity is yin?
   Problem-solving
   Daydreaming —

8. Which relationship with money is yang?
   Earning money —
   Spending money

9. Which structure has a yin form?
   The Empire State Building —
   The Great Pyramid

10. Yang produces heat. Yin produces cold. True or false?

11. Between water and fire, which has a yin effect?

12. In which environment do we find yang plant life?
    A northern climate —
    A tropical climate

13. Which type of hair is yin?
    The hair growing on your head —
    The hair growing on your body

14. Which activity makes us yang?
    Lying on the beach
    Shoveling snow —

15. Brightness is yin, darkness is yang. True or false?

16. Which of our senses is yin?
    The sense of touch
    The sense of hearing —

17. Which occupation is yang?
    Musician
    Construction worker —

18. If you want to make yourself yin, to which country would
    you travel?
    Russia
    Brazil —

19. Which part of the atom is yang?
    Proton —
    Electron

20. Which hormone is yin?
    Estrogen —
    Testosterone

21. The front of the body is yin. The back is yang. True or false?

22. Which type of reproductive cell is yin?
    Egg
    Sperm —

23. During which phase of the moon does energy move in a yin
    direction?
    Full moon —
    New moon

24. Which type of fingers are yang?
    Long fingers
    Short fingers —

Congratulations! You have now completed the Yin Yang Quiz.
Answers on the next page.

Answers to the Yin Yang Quiz

1. In comparing a stone to water, which has a yin form?
   Answer: Water
   Water is more diffuse and expanded (yin) than a stone. A stone is compact and solid (yang). When you throw a stone in a pond, it sinks (yang.)

2. In comparing water to air, which has a yang form?
   Answer: Water
   Water is more dense and compact (yang) than air. That is why bubbles rise to the surface (yin.) Water is yin compared to a stone and yang compared to air. Things are yin or yang only in relation to other things.

3. Which of the following moves in a yin direction?
   Evaporating mist
   Falling rain
   Answer: Evaporating mist
   Mist is more expanded than rain. It moves upward and outward (yin.) Raindrops are more condensed. They fall downward and gather to form puddles (yang.) Like everything else, water always cycles between yin and yang.

4. During which time of day is energy moving in a yang direction?
   Sunrise
   Sunset
   Answer: Sunset
   Upward motion (sunrise) is expansive (yin.) Downward motion (sunset) is contractive (yang.) In the morning people get up. The sun causes things to expand. At night, people lie down. Things become more contracted. Day after day, yin changes into yang and yang changes into yin, in an alternating cycle.

5. Which of the following occupies a yin position?
   Apple seeds
   The skin of an apple

Answer: The skin of an apple
Expansive force pushes things out toward the periphery.
Contractive force pushes things in toward the center. Apple
seeds form at the center. The skin forms on the outside. The
core is yang, the skin is yin.

6. Which group of people is yang?
   A team playing a game
   The spectators watching them
   Answer: A team playing a game
   The players occupy a central or inside position (yang). The
   people watching the game are outside the action in a
   peripheral position (yin.) Fans watching the game on
   television are more peripheral or yin than those attending it.

7. Which activity is yin?
   Problem-solving
   Daydreaming
   Answer: Daydreaming
   Problem-solving requires concentration and focus (yang.)
   Daydreaming occurs when you let your mind wander (yin.)
   When you daydream, you unfocus your eyes and look into
   the distance (yin.)

8. Which relationship with money is yang?
   Earning money
   Spending money
   Answer: Earning money
   In order for money flow toward you (yang), you need to
   contract and focus your energy. When you relax and expand,
   money tends to flow outward (yin.) Work is thus more yang
   than relaxation. However, what is yin for the buyer is yang
   for the seller, and vice-versa. Whether something is yin or
   yang depends on your point of view.

9. Which structure has a yin form?
   The Empire State Building
   The Great Pyramid
   Answer: The Empire State Building
   Things with a vertical form expand upward (yin). Things with
   horizontal forms contract downward (yang). Tall
   buildings are yin, squat buildings are yang.

10. Yang produces heat. Yin produces cold. True or false?
    Answer: True
    Heat is a property of yang or contraction. In order to light a
    match, you need to rub it against a surface. If the match
    doesn't come into contact with something, it won't ignite.
    Contact (yang) produces heat; separation (yin) produces
    cold.

11. Between water and fire, which has a yin effect?
    Answer: Water
    Adding water to something makes it expand (yin.) So does
    soaking it. Fire makes things contract (yang.) When you
    burn logs in a fireplace they eventually contract into ashes.
    Roasting seeds in a dry skillet makes them hard and
    crunchy (yang.) Soaking them makes them softer (yin.)

12. In which environment do we find yang plant life?
    A northern climate
    A tropical climate
    Answer: A northern climate
    Cold weather (yin) causes things to contract. Hot weather
    (yang) makes things expand. As we approach the North
    Pole, vegetation becomes smaller and more contracted
    (yang.) At the equator, vegetation is lush and expanded
    (yin.)

13. Which type of hair is yin?
    The hair growing on your head
    The hair growing on your body
    Answer: The hair growing on your head
    Head hair grows in an upward direction (yin.) Body hair
    grows in a downward direction (yang.) Head hair is
    generally softer (yin), while body hair is coarser (yang.)

14. Which activity makes us yang?
    Lying on the beach
    Shoveling snow
    Answer: Shoveling snow
    As with other forms of physical activity, shoveling snow
    requires contraction and tension of the muscles (yang.)
    Lying on the beach causes our muscles to relax (yin.)

15. Brightness is yin, darkness is yang. True or false?

Answer: False
In the universe, light is generated by tiny condensed points known as stars (yang.) The expanse of space (yin) that surrounds them is dark. Light is a property of contraction, darkness a property of expansion.

16. Which of our senses is yin?
   The sense of touch
   The sense of hearing
   Answer: The sense of hearing
   Our ears process sound waves which are more diffuse and expanded (yin) than the physical objects processed by our touch receptors. The sense of touch requires contact with an object (yang). Sounds can originate at a great distance from the hearer (yin.)

17. Which occupation is yang?
   Musician
   Construction worker
   Answer: Construction worker
   A construction worker deals with physical objects (yang). A musician deals with sound vibrations (yin.) Construction work usually involves heavy lifting and other forms of intense physical exertion (yang.)

18. If you want to make yourself yin, to which country would you travel?
   Russia
   Brazil
   Answer: Brazil
   Brazil's hot climate causes things to expand (yin.) Russia's cold makes things contract (yang.) Foods grown in a hot climate are yin. When we eat them, we become yin. Foods grown in a cold climate are yang. When we eat them, we become yang.

19. Which part of the atom is yang?
   Proton
   Electron
   Answer: Proton
   Protons are found at the center of the atom (yang.) Electrons spiral around the periphery (yin.) Protons have a greater density of mass (yang) than electrons. Electrons, which have

practically no mass, exist at the boundary between matter (yang) and energy (yin.)

20. Which hormone is yin?
Estrogen
Testosterone
Answer: Estrogen
At puberty, estrogen causes the female body to become softer and more expanded (yin.) At puberty, testosterone makes the male body more lean and compact (yang.) Testosterone stimulates the development of body hair and aggressive behavior (both yang.)

21. The front of the body is yin. The back is yang. True or false?
Answer: True
The front of the body is softer and more expanded (yin) than the back. Running down the center of the back is the spine, which is made of condensed minerals (yang.)

22. Which type of reproductive cell is yin?
Egg
Sperm
Answer: Sperm
Sperm are lighter and more diffuse (yin) than the condensed ovum. Sperm are produced through a process of differentiation (yin.) One ejaculation contains millions. Sperm move in an upward direction (yin.) The ovum moves downward (yang.) Egg and sperm are strongly polarized. That is why they are strongly attracted.

23. During which phase of the moon does energy move in a yin direction?
Full moon
New moon
Answer: Full moon
The brightness of the full moon (yang) causes energy to move upward and outward (yin.) We discharge more actively when the moon is full. The darkness of the new moon (yin) causes energy to be held inside (yang.) We tend to be more stable and centered when the moon is new.

24. Which type of fingers are yang?
Long fingers

Short fingers
Answer: Short fingers
The fingers extend outward (yin) from the palm. Long
fingers indicate a greater degree of expanding energy. People with long fingers are often comfortable with music and
other artistic pursuits (yin.) A person with short fingers is
often more comfortable with physical activity (yang.)

Evaluation and Guidance

1-8 Correct: Don't be discouraged. Since yin changes to yang, and
yang changes to yin, you can definitely rise to the top. Congratulations! Please continue your studies. Read this book two more times.
Also read *The Book of Macrobiotics* by Michio Kushi, *Essential Ohsawa*
edited by Carl Ferré, and *Learning from Salmon* by Herman Aihara.
Chew well; up to 50 times per mouthful (chewing strengthens mental
clarity.) Eat regular meals based on whole grains and vegetables.
Drink a little less liquid, especially if your hands are moist. Skip
breakfast on occasion. Practice cooking daily. Exercise regularly (activity increases blood flow to the brain.) Spend time outdoors. Increase your contact with nature. Try to be less conceptual and more
practical. Trust your intuition more. Make a list of complementary/
opposites in your immediate environment.

9-16 Correct: Don't be content. Strive to improve. Continue to
think and study. Read classics such as the Tao Teh Ching, the I
Ching, the Yellow Emperor's Classic, and others from East and West.
Try to find examples of yin and yang (complementary/opposites) in
these and other works of literature, art, and philosophy. Keep grains
and vegetables as your principal foods. Chew well, and study and
observe natural cycles. Review your daily life in terms of yin and
yang. Reflect on whether or not your diet is balanced. Practice cooking regularly. Try not to overeat. Exercise daily.

17-24 Correct: Don't be overconfident. Try not to relax too much.
(This is especially true if you achieved a perfect score.) The higher
you become, the greater distance you have to fall. Therefore, eat well
and keep a humble attitude. Continually seek new challenges. Use
your understanding to invent something new. Reflect on your life
dream. Come up with original answers to the riddles of science and
philosophy, life and nature. Think about how yin and yang can be
used to create a healthy and peaceful world. Make yourself and those
around you healthy and peaceful.

Resources

Edward Esko teaches macrobiotics, holistic health, and planetary ecology internationally. He is a co-founder of One Peaceful World Press and author of *Healing Planet Earth, Notes from the Boundless Frontier, The Pulse of Life, Basics and Benefits of Macrobiotics,* and many other books. He lives with his wife, Wendy, a macrobiotic cooking teacher, and his family in Becket, Massachusetts.

The One Peaceful World Society is an international information network and macrobiotic friendship society founded by Michio Kushi. Membership is $30/year for individuals ($40 outside of the U.S. and Canada) and $50 for families, and benefits include the quarterly *One Peaceful World Journal,* free books from One Peaceful World Press, and discounts on books and study materials. To join or for information, please contact One Peaceful World, Box 10, Becket, MA 01223, toll-free (888) 322-4095, telephone (413) 623-2322, fax (413) 623-6042, e-mail opw@macrobiotics.org, website: www.macrobiotics.org

The Kushi Institute is an educational center for macrobiotic and holistic studies. For information on programs, please contact Kushi Institute, Box 7, Becket, MA 01223, (413) 623-5741, Fax (413) 623-8827, e-mail kushi@macrobiotics.org, website www.macrobiotics.org

emacrobiotics.com is the web site founded by Edward and Wendy Esko. It features a calendar of macrobiotic events, monthly recipes, a macrobiotic bookstore, a natural product showcase and store, and an interactive version of the Yin Yang Quiz (Macrobiotics Interactive). Edward Esko can be contacted at (413) 623-5645. Email esko@berkshire.net

Index